Marco Marker
He's a joker who lo
messing about, bu
always means well
if he sometimes ge
things wrong.

Splodge,
oooooooo
oooooooh!

Philippa Feltpen
A real peacemaker, she
helps keep the other
Pens in order by sorting
out arguments and
giving good advice.

Enter ...

Waxy Max
He's very sporty and
football mad. On the
outside, he's tough,
but underneath he's
got the biggest heart.

Squiggle and Splodge
The Scribble twins! They're
both quiet, both shy. Although
they may not look alike, they
do almost everything together.

Pens

Helping you to get
to know God more

Pumpkin Party

Written by
Alexa Tewkesbury

Pens discover that every day
can be a time to celebrate God's
love, even though some people
like to celebrate Halloween.
A short story followed by five
days of Bible readings, thoughts
and prayers, based on the
adventures of Paul, to help
young children learn to trust
God to look after them.

What's inside?

Candles, Pumpkins, and the BIG Surprise

One chilly autumn morning, Charlotte knocked on Henry Highlighter's front door.

Hello, Henry.

Would you like to help me today? I'm getting ready for a BIG surprise!

'I can't tell you that,' Charlotte smiled. 'Otherwise it wouldn't be a surprise, would it?'

Henry looked at his calendar. It was the 31st day of October.

'Mmm …' he wondered. 'What's surprising about that?'

Then –

'Of course!' Henry thought. 'It's Halloween! *That's* what Charlotte must be getting ready for!'

But Henry didn't tell Charlotte he'd guessed. He didn't want to spoil her BIG surprise.

Henry found the sheets in no time.

'Mmm …' he wondered. 'Why does Charlotte need white sheets?'

Then –

'Of course!' he thought. 'At Halloween, children sometimes dress up as ghosts or other things that can look a bit scary. Charlotte must be going to use the sheets to make costumes for us!'

But Henry didn't tell Charlotte he'd guessed. He didn't want to spoil her BIG surprise.

sheets

First, they stopped at the greengrocer's. Charlotte bought two plump, orange pumpkins.

Next, they called at the corner shop. Charlotte bought a box of candles.

'Mmm …' Henry wondered. 'Why does Charlotte need pumpkins and candles?'

Then –

'Of course!' he thought. 'At Halloween people often carve scary faces into pumpkins. Then they put a burning candle inside and the face lights up! Charlotte must be going to make pumpkin lanterns.'

But Henry didn't tell Charlotte he'd guessed. He didn't want to spoil her BIG surprise.

Back home again, Charlotte unfolded some orange cloth.

'Let's cut some squares out of my cloth, Henry,' said Charlotte.

Then Charlotte showed Henry how to sew the squares into little bags.

'Mmm …' Henry wondered. 'Why does Charlotte need bags?'

Then –

'Of course!' he thought. 'At Halloween, children sometimes go out with their parents to knock on people's doors. Then they ask for treats and hope to be given sweets. That must be what the bags are for. To put our treats in!'

But Henry didn't tell Charlotte he'd guessed. He didn't want to spoil her BIG surprise.

'Would you help me with one more thing, please, Henry?' asked Charlotte. 'I've made some invitations for our Pens friends. Let's go and deliver them.'

Henry read the words on the invitations excitedly:

Come to Charlotte's house tonight for a BIG surprise! See you there.

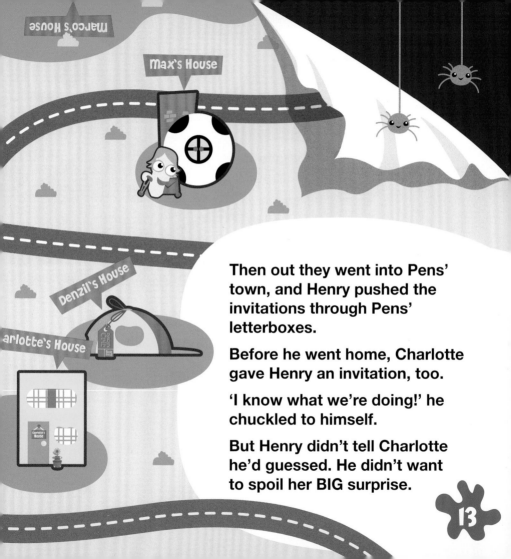

Then out they went into Pens' town, and Henry pushed the invitations through Pens' letterboxes.

Before he went home, Charlotte gave Henry an invitation, too.

'I know what we're doing!' he chuckled to himself.

But Henry didn't tell Charlotte he'd guessed. He didn't want to spoil her BIG surprise.

13

The white sheets Henry had found for Charlotte were spread out on the floor. And although Henry looked and looked, he couldn't see a pumpkin lantern anywhere.

16

'But, Charlotte,' Henry frowned, 'I thought the sheets were for us to dress up in as spooky ghosts.'

'No!' laughed Charlotte. 'Some people dress up at Halloween. But that's not what *we're* doing.'

'But, Charlotte,' Henry replied, 'I thought you were going to make the pumpkins into lanterns with scary faces.'

'No!' said Charlotte. 'Some people make pumpkin lanterns at Halloween. But that's not what *we're* doing.'

'Oh,' answered Henry. 'Why not?'

17

Charlotte looked thoughtful.
'Some people *do* do scary things at
Halloween,' she explained. 'But what
God hopes we'll do on this day and
every day is think about *Him* instead.
God doesn't want us to scare people
or to feel afraid ourselves. He wants
us to be His friends, and to trust Him
to look after us.'

Then Charlotte smiled, 'Are you all
hungry? We're going to have an
indoor picnic.'

The white sheets on the floor were
to sit on. The pumpkins had been
made into hot, tasty soup.

After the picnic, Charlotte gave a present to each Pen.

'Those are the bags we made!' Henry cried.

'Yes,' beamed Charlotte. 'Inside each bag is one of the candles we bought. Let's all keep our candles safe – to remind us of God's love.'

'How can candles do that?' asked Henry.

'When a candle burns in the darkness,' replied Charlotte, 'its light means it isn't dark any more. God's love is like that – a light in the dark for everyone who trusts Him. We never need to be worried or afraid. Now, isn't that a brilliantly BIG surprise!'

Paul was one of God's best friends.

He talked about God. He wrote about God.

He wanted everyone to know how much God loved them.

But God's enemies didn't like what Paul said. They made him their prisoner. Then they put him on a ship that was sailing to a city called Rome.

A stormy wind began to blow.

The ship rocked and rolled.

After a little while, the sailors found a harbour where they could shelter.

Paul shook his head. 'The weather is very bad,' he said. 'We should stay here until it's better. Then we'll be safe.'

Even though Paul was a prisoner, he didn't want anyone on the ship to be hurt.

What's the weather like when it's stormy?

Pens Prayer

Lord God, I love being Your friend. Please help me to tell others about You. Amen.

The captain and his sailors didn't want to stay in the harbour. They wanted to get on with their journey.

So no one listened to Paul.

'Let's go as soon as we can,' they said.

Some time later, the wind began to blow a little more softly.

The ship rocked and rolled a little more gently.

And they set sail for the city of Rome once more.

But before long, the storm came back. Again, the wind howled. Once more, the waves grew huge.

The sailors were frightened. 'What shall we do?' they cried.

No one listened to Paul, so the ship got into trouble again.

Why is it important to listen to the people who care about you?

Pens Prayer

Father God, thank You for speaking to me through stories in the Bible. Please teach me to listen to You. Amen.

'… take heart! Not one of you will lose his life …' (Acts 27 v 22)

Kind words

Day after day the storm roared across the sea.

'We must stop the ship falling apart!' shouted the captain. So the sailors threw long ropes around it and tied them tightly.

'We mustn't let the ship sink!' shouted the captain. So the sailors made it lighter. They dropped whatever they could over the sides into the sea.

'If only you'd listened to me,' Paul said. 'Then we wouldn't be caught in this storm.'

But Paul didn't seem cross or scared.

Instead, he added kindly, 'Don't worry. We'll be all right. God's going to save us.'

The sailors were afraid – but Paul knew God would keep them all safe.

How can you learn to trust God more?

Pens Prayer

Dear Lord, You've promised to take care of me. Please help me to trust You. Amen

The stormy wind still blew. The huge waves still crashed loudly against the ship.

But Paul *still* wasn't frightened.

He said to the sailors, 'Listen! God sent an angel to me last night. The angel told me not to be afraid because God is looking after all of us. And I trust God,' Paul smiled. 'I know He loves me. You must all trust Him, too.'

The sailors listened to Paul but they couldn't stop feeling afraid. They didn't know God as well as Paul did. They didn't understand how much God loved them.

Paul trusted God because he knew that God loved him.

How did God comfort and encourage Paul?

Pens Prayer

Thank You, Lord, that if I'm ever worried or scared You're always there to comfort me. Please show me how to comfort others too. Amen.

The sailors hadn't eaten anything for a long time. They were too busy trying to save the ship.

'You must have food to keep up your energy,' Paul told them.

Then he took some bread and said thank You to God for it.

At last the sailors realised how much Paul loved and trusted God. They even began to feel better because Paul was so sure they were safe in God's hands.

One day, the ship was blown towards an island. The sailors had to swim to the shore, but they all arrived safely.

Just as God had promised.

The sailors felt less afraid when they saw how Paul trusted God completely.

How can you show your friends that you love and trust God?

Pens Prayer

Father God, Your love is amazing! Thank You that You take care of

Pens titles

More *Pens* for you to enjoy

* Friends
* Father God
* Following Jesus
* Really Special
* Trusting God
* Helping and Serving
* Big and Small

* God's Book
* God's Love
* God Cares
* God's Heroes
* Thank You God
* God's Peace
* Praise God!

* Yes God
* Sorry God!
* Hand in Hand
* Belonging to God
* Talking to God
* Help!

Pens Specials

32-page full colour booklets, 148x148mm

Watch us come to life as animated cartoons at www.cwr.org.uk/pens

Pens Special! Christmas

The Pens characters tell the Christmas story to make Jesus' birth real and memorable for young children.

Pens Special! Easter

Help young children understand the true meaning of Easter.

Pens Special! Starting School

Help children start school confidently, knowing that God goes there with them.

Available online, or from Christian bookshops.
For current prices visit **www.cwr.org.uk/store**